TRAIN TRIVIA

FOR RAILFANS

220 QUESTIONS & ANSWERS

RAILROAD BRAINTEASERS
FOR TRAIN LOVERS OF ALL AGES

TRAIN TRIVIA

#1. Which locomotive holds the record for the heaviest steam locomotive ever built?
    a. Union Pacific Big Boy
    b. Russian P36
    c. British Rail
    d. Soviet Pobeda

#2. Which country was the first to introduce the concept of high-speed rail?
    a. Japan
    b. France
    c. Germany
    d. United States

#3. What is the maximum speed of the Shanghai Maglev (fastest train in the world)?
    a. 186 mph
    b. 249 mph
    c. 267 mph
    d. 375 mph

#4. What is the world's first commercial monorail system named?
    a. Wuppertal Suspension Railway
    b. Schwebebahn Dresden
    c. H-Bahn
    d. Lartigue

TRAIN TRIVIA

#5. What was the steepest operating mainline grade in the U.S. until 2001 when it was removed from service?
    a. 4.7% Saluda Grade (North Carolina)
    b. 3.3% Raton Pass (New Mexico)
    c. 2.8% Madison Incline (Indiana)
    d. 4.9% Boston Central Pass (Massachusetts)

#6. What is the name of the first high-speed rail system in the United States?
    a. Acela Express
    b. California High-Speed Rail
    c. Texas Central Railway
    d. Florida High-Speed Rail

#7. What locomotive set the 1938 steam locomotive world speed record?
    a. Mallard
    b. Flying Scotsman
    c. Aberdeen
    d. Sceptre

#8. What country boasts the world's highest railway line?
    a. China
    b. India
    c. Bolivia
    d. Peru

TRAIN TRIVIA

#9. What is the name of the world's longest railway tunnel?

    a. Gotthard Base Tunnel

    b. Seikan Tunnel

    c. Channel Tunnel

    d. Lötschberg Base Tunnel

#10. Which train holds the record for the fastest commercial train service in the world?

    a. Japanese Shinkansen

    b. Chinese CRH380A

    c. French TGV

    d. German ICE

#11. What is the name of the train that connects Paris to Istanbul?

    a. Orient Express

    b. Istanbul-Paris Connection

    c. Simplon Orient Express

    d. Paris-Istanbul Express

#12. What is the highest recorded speed record for a steam locomotive?

    a. 118 mph by Sceptre

    b. 126mph by Mallard

    c. 138mph by Flying Scotsman

    d. 127 mph by Aberdeen

TRAIN TRIVIA

#13. What is the name of the oldest surviving steam locomotive in the world?

    a. Puffing Billy
    b. Locomotion No. 1
    c. The Rocket
    d. The Salamanca

#14. What was the name of the first steam locomotive to run on rails in the United States?

    a. Best Friend of Charleston
    b. Tom Thumb
    c. John Bull
    d. DeWitt Clinton

#15. What steam locomotive pulled Abraham Lincoln's funeral train?

    a. Jupiter
    b. General
    c. Leviathan
    d. Old Nashville

#16. Which steam locomotive is the largest and most powerful ever built?

    a. Big Boy
    b. Challenger
    c. Union Pacific 4014
    d. Union Pacific 3985

TRAIN TRIVIA

#17. Which Art Deco design diesel locomotive served on the Chicago, Burlington and Quincy Railroad?
    a. Hudson
    b. Zephyr
    c. Niagara
    d. Berkshire

#18. Which famous steam locomotive pulled the Freedom Train during WW2?
    a. Daylight
    b. Challenger
    c. J Class
    d. Reading T-1

#19. Which is known for it's fleet of heritage locomotives, each painted in a different historic paint scheme?
    a. Union Pacific
    b. Norfolk Southern
    c. BNSF Railway
    d. CSX Transportation

#20. What is the purpose of the locomotive's horn?
    a. To scare animals off the tracks
    b. To signal the crew
    c. To warn pedestrians and vehicles at crossings
    d. To communicate with other trains

TRAIN TRIVIA

#21. Which is known for it's yellow bonnet locomotives?
a. Union Pacific
b. Norfolk Southern
c. BNSF Railway
d. CSX Transportation

#22. What part of a train's system helps the train slow down or stop?
a. Cowcatcher
b. Bell
c. Brake Shoe
d. Headlight

#23. Which type of railcar is used for carrying liquids like oil or chemicals?
a. Boxcar
b. Flatcar
c. Tank Car
d. Hopper Car

#24. What connects train cars together?
a. Coupler
b. Connector
c. Linker
d. Hitcher

TRAIN TRIVIA

#25. Which famous train travels a luxurious route from Cape Town to Pretoria?
    a. Blue Train
    b. Rovos Rail
    c. Palace on Wheels
    d. Maharajas' Express

#26. Who developed the first practical steam locomotive boiler which improved steam engine efficiency?
    a. James Watt
    b. George Stephenson
    c. Richard Trevithick
    d. Timothy Hackworth

#27. What purpose does a cowcatcher (pilot) serve?
    a. To keep the train balanced
    b. To catch cows that wander onto the tracks
    c. To deflect debris from the track
    d. To improve aerodynamics

#28. Which part of a steam locomotive distributes steam to the cylinders to move the train?
    a. Boiler
    b. Tender
    c. Piston
    d. Valve gear

TRAIN TRIVIA

#29. Which railroad operated the famous "Super Chief" train from Chicago to Los Angeles?
   a. Union Pacific
   b. Central Pacific
   c. Southern Pacific
   d. Santa Fe

#30. Which part stores and supplies coal or oil to the firebox on a train?
   a. Boiler
   b. Tender
   c. Tank car
   d. Fuel car

#31. Which company operated the Hiawatha train?
   a. Union Pacific
   b. Central Pacific
   c. New York Central
   d. Milwaukee Road

#32. In the United States, what is the freight train length legal limit?
   a. 120 cars
   b. there is no legal limit
   c. 220 cars
   d. 300 cars

TRAIN TRIVIA

#33. Which is not a real Canadian railroad?
   a. Ontario Northland
   b. Canadian Pacific
   c. Alberta Road
   d. Via-Rail

#34. "Folsom Prison Blues" and _____ were train hits by singer Johnny Cash?
   a. Train My Heart
   b. All Aboard
   c. Train of Love
   d. High Speed Train

#35. Which famous train was featured in a 1954 film starring Marlon Brando (and also the film name)?
   a. Orient Express
   b. Trans-Siberian Express
   c. The Wild One
   d. 20th Century Limited

#36. What is the most common scale for model trains?
   a. HO scale
   b. N scale
   c. O scale
   d. G scale

#37. What does the term "DCC" stand for in model railroading?

 a. Digital Command Control
 b. Direct Current Control
 c. Diesel Control Center
 d. Dual Cab Control

#38. Which material is commonly used for the scenery on a model train layout?

 a. Plaster
 b. Wood
 c. Styrofoam
 d. All of the above

#39. In the famous Harry Potter book series, what is the name of the train which takes students to school?

 a. University Rail
 b. Hogwarts Express
 c. Tripoli Transport
 d. Castle Express

#40. What is a "yard goat" in train slang?

 a. Small locomotive used for moving cars in yard
 b. Railway worker who tends to the yard
 c. Type of freight car used for carrying livestock
 d. Slang term for a slow-moving train

TRAIN TRIVIA

#41. Which scale is larger, HO or N?
    a. HO
    b. N
    c. They are the same size
    d. It depends on the manufacturer

#42. The box with windows on top of a caboose roof is called what?
    a. Terrarium
    b. Cupola
    c. Lookout
    d. Platform

#43. How many passenger platforms does Grand Central Station in New York City have?
    a. 57
    b. 32
    c. 44
    d. 71

#44. During the peak of the Trans-Siberian Railway construction during the 1890s, how many workers were employed?
    a. 9,500
    b. 85,000
    c. 17,450
    d. 51,000

#45. Which of these railfans created the Thomas the Tank Engine series for his son?
    a. Walt Disney
    b. Reverend W. Awdry
    c. John Wayne
    d. Ringo Starr

#46. Which of these helps overcome the obstacle of altitude/height on a railroad?
    a. Tunnel
    b. Switchback
    c. Suspension Bridge
    d. Turntable

#47. Signal systems not only are used to communicate the speed of a train but also the what?
    a. Direction
    b. Route
    c. Size
    d. Weight

#48. What train feature is now obsolete?
    a. Horn
    b. Signals
    c. Caboose
    d. Tanker car

TRAIN TRIVIA

#49. Which train became famous for being the target of a train robbery in the U.S. in 1877?
    a. The General
    b. Union Pacific No. 119
    c. Tom Thumb
    d. Jupiter

#50. What was the name of the first luxury sleeping car introduced in 1865 in America?
    a. Pullman Car
    b. Orient Express
    c. Thunderbolt
    d. The Times

#51. Which country was the first to introduce regular passenger train services in 1830?
    a. United States
    b. France
    c. United Kingdom
    d. Germany

#52. What was the original purpose of the invention of the first trains in the early 19th century?
    a. Military transportation
    b. Passenger transportation
    c. Freight transportation
    d. Amusement rides/entertainment

TRAIN TRIVIA

#53. Which technology does the Shanghai Maglev Train utilize?

    a. Steam

    b. Battery power

    c. Diesel

    d. Magnetic levitation

#54. Which country is home to Thalys, a high-speed rail service known for it's red trains?

    a. Canada

    b. Germany

    c. Belgium

    d. China

#55. Which train part controls the flow of steam to the cylinders to propel the train?

    a. Valve gear

    b. Regulator

    c. Throttle

    d. Boiler

#56. Which company was known for it's luxury "Broadway Limited" train?

    a. Union Pacific

    b. Central Pacific

    c. Milwaukee Road

    d. Pennsylvania Railroad

TRAIN TRIVIA

#57. Who invented the steam whistle?
    a. Thomas Edison
    b. James Watt
    c. Timothy Hackworth
    d. Adrian Stephens

#58. Most modern rail cars can have a gross weight of how many pounds each?
    a. 4,700
    b. 103,000
    c. 286,000
    d. 314,500

#59. When a train uses it's version of "cruise control", what percent of fuel savings results?
    a. less than 1%
    b. 7%
    c. 3-5%
    d. 10-12%

#60. How many tons of freight do American railroads haul each year?
    a. 67 million tons
    b. 429 million tons
    c. 1 billion tons
    d. 1.7 billion tons

TRAIN TRIVIA

#61. How many railroads currently operate in the U.S.?
- a. 217
- b. 431
- c. 580
- d. Over 600

#62. Some locomotives have a Positive Train Control (PTC) system onboard which does what?
- a. Keeps the train balanced on the tracks
- b. Operates the trains without human engineers
- c. Automatically stops a train to avoid collisions
- d. Acts as GPS letting management know location

#63. These are used to help in the maintenance of railroad tracks in the U.S.?
- a. Walkie talkies
- b. Drones
- c. Super strong magnets
- d. Magnifying glasses

#64. The name of the platform for the locomotive driver is called the what?
- a. Kingplate
- b. Stepboard
- c. Railpin
- d. Footplate

TRAIN TRIVIA

#65. What is the job title of the train driver?
   a. Pilot
   b. Conductor
   c. Engineer
   d. Lead Driver

#66. What year did the Great Train Robbery occur?
   a. 1942
   b. 1957
   c. 1963
   d. 1971

#67. What is the train number on the side of the Thomas the Tank Engine Character?
   a. 4
   b. 7
   c. 1
   d. 15

#68. On average, railroads are how many times more efficient than semi trucks?
   a. 2x
   b. 3-4x
   c. 10x
   d. 20x

TRAIN TRIVIA

#69. A single train can carry the same amount as how many semi freight trucks?
    a. 80
    b. 120
    c. 230
    d. 300

#70. Amtrak began operations in which year?
    a. 1954
    b. 1969
    c. 1971
    d. 1984

#71. Which was never used as an Amtrak promotional campaign slogan?
    a. "America's Getting Into Training"
    b. "See America At See Level"
    c. "Training To The Future"
    d. "Making 500 Destinations A Far Better Ride"

#72. On an average day, Amtrak carries how many passengers systemwide?
    a. 36,000
    b. 54,000
    c. 89,000
    d. 107,000

TRAIN TRIVIA

#73. The Empire Builder makes how many stops over 8 states on it's route?

    a. 40

    b. 24

    c. 56

    d. 45

#74. How many Amtrak stations are listed as National Historic Places?

    a. none

    b. three

    c. seven

    d. ten

#75. The smallest community in the U.S. served by Amtrak has how many residents?

    a. 5

    b. 247

    c. 2,100

    d. 3,080

#76. The fastest train in the Western Hemisphere is what?

    a. Acela

    b. Big Boy

    c. Raceway

    d. Commander

TRAIN TRIVIA

#77. Which country has the largest railway network in the world?
- a. Canada
- b. United States
- c. China
- d. Australia

#78. How many miles of railroad track are in the U.S.?
- a. 64,000 miles
- b. 118,000
- c. 155,000
- d. 196,000

#79. In the U.S. rail network, what is the % of freight routes to passenger routes?
- a. 20% freight / 80% passenger
- b. 35% freight / 65% passenger
- c. 60% freight / 40% passenger
- d. 80% freight / 20% passenger

#80. Which is the oldest railway in the world still in use since 1758?
- a. Shinjuku Station (Tokyo, Japan)
- b. Middleton Railway (Leeds, England)
- c. Glasgow Station (Glasgow, Scotland)
- d. Grand Central Station (New York City, U.S.)

TRAIN TRIVIA

#81. The longest journey you can take by train crosses 2 continents from Portugal to Singapore at a cost of:
- a. $900
- b. $1,300
- c. $7,000
- d. $15,420

#82. The longest direct train service in the world is in Russia on the Trans-Siberian route. What is the total time, mileage and stops on this direct route?
- a. 84 hrs / 3,642 miles / 72 stops
- b. 113 hrs / 4,421 miles / 94 stops
- c. 166 hrs / 5,772 miles / 142 stops
- d. 192 hrs / 8,102 miles / 173 stops

#83. America's oldest operating railroad (1832) is named?
- a. Strasburg Railroad
- b. Glencoe Railways
- c. Soo Line Railroad
- d. Milwaukee Road

#84. Shinjuku Station in Tokyo, Japan is the world's busiest train station with how many daily passengers?
- a. 864,000
- b. 1.1 million
- c. 2.4 million
- d. 3.6 million

TRAIN TRIVIA

#85. In what year were Australia's coasts linked for travel by train:
    a. 1917
    b. 1958
    c. 1970
    d. 1996

#86. Which train travels on the world's longest straight stretch of railroad, spanning 303 miles?
    a. Milwaukee Road
    b. Indian Pacific
    c. Canadian Rail
    d. Strasburg Railroad

#87. The highest railway bridge in the world stands 98 feet higher than the Eiffel Tower and is located where?
    a. Switzerland
    b. Belgium
    c. China
    d. India

#88. The longest train station name is "Llanfairpwllgwyngyllgogerychwyrndrobwllllantysiliogo gogoch" and is located where?
    a. El Paso, Texas
    b. Fairbanks, Alaska
    c. Wales, England
    d. Alberta, Canada

TRAIN TRIVIA

#89. Which countries currently have no railway system:
   a. Kuwait
   b. Iceland
   c. Malta
   d. all of the above

#90. How many miles of railway track are there in the entire world?
   a. 609,000
   b. 807,000
   c. 924,000
   d. 1 million

#91. Under Grand Central Station there is a secret train platform known as what?
   a. Area 531
   b. Track 61
   c. Underground Rail
   d. Platform 9 3/4

#92. Extreme temperatures, such as what temps can cause steel railroad tracks to buckle?
   a. Over 80 degrees F
   b. Over 95 degrees F
   c. Over 100 degrees F
   d. Over 120 degrees F

TRAIN TRIVIA

#93. In the early 2000s, New York City disposed of how many old subway trains by sinking them in the ocean:
    a. 72
    b. 348
    c. 1,072
    d. 2,580

#94. In the U.S., how often is a person or vehicle hit by a train?
    a. every hour
    b. every three hours
    c. every day
    d. every week

#95. In the U.S., who owns the railroad tracks?
    a. individual land owners
    b. the government
    c. train companies
    d. Federal Railroad Administration

#96. When a freight train is traveling at 55 mph, how long does it take it to stop?
    a. 500 feet
    b. 1 mile
    c. 2 miles
    d. 3 miles

TRAIN TRIVIA

#97. What percentage of train routes in England go through London:
- a. 25%
- b. 60%
- c. 70%
- d. 95%

#98. The total contact between train wheels and track is the size of what?
- a. penny
- b. quarter
- c. silver dollar
- d. grapefruit

#99. The longest train station platform in England is the size of how many football fields?
- a. one
- b. three
- c. six
- d. ten

#100. How many feet long does the Big Boy engine measure?
- a. 84 feet
- b. 97 feet
- c. 132 feet
- d. 151 feet

TRAIN TRIVIA

#101. How much horsepower did the most powerful steam engines (like Big Boy) generate at peak output?
    a. over 4000 hp
    b. over 5100 hp
    c. over 6000 hp
    d. over 7300 hp

#102. Big Boy engine was designed to move large amounts of freight during which war for Union Pacific?
    a. Civil War
    b. WW1
    c. Vietnam War
    d. WW2

#103. Amtrak trains typically run at what range of speed?
    a. 60 - 90 mph
    b. 80 - 125 mph
    c. 100 - 140 mph
    d. 125 - 160 mph

#104. What does the word "intermodal" mean?
    a. freight is moved via both steam & diesel trains
    b. freight is moved between coastal cities
    c. freight is moved via 2+ ways (ship, train, truck, plane)
    d. freight is moved via helicopter

TRAIN TRIVIA

#105. What is the nickname for the Japanese Shinkansen high-speed train?
    a. Whizz train
    b. Bullet train
    c. Speed Demon
    d. Tornado train

#106. What city in the U.S. has the oldest and steepest funicular railway you can still ride?
    a. Boston
    b. Philadelphia
    c. Trenton
    d. Pittsburgh

#107. Gordon, James, Percy & Emily are all characters from what popular children's train book series?
    a. Walter And His Whistle
    b. Thomas The Tank Engine
    c. The Little Engine That Could
    d. Tootle

#108. The raised observation seat in the caboose car was sometimes called the "_____'s Seat"?
    a. King
    b. Angel
    c. Balloon
    d. Rapunzel

TRAIN TRIVIA

#109. The oldest subway tunnel in North America is located in which city?

    a. San Francisco

    b. New York

    c. Boston

    d. Atlanta

#110. The world's oldest continuously operating streetcar line is located in which city?

    a. San Francisco

    b. Florence

    c. New Orleans

    d. London

#111. Stephenson's Rocket was not a spaceship, but an earlier form of what type of vehicle?

    a. Biplane

    b. Steam train

    c. Diesel train

    d. Freight ship

#112. Which rail-based "2004 Board Game of the Year" shares it's name with a Beatles song?

    a. Yellow Submarine

    b. Here Comes the Sun

    c. Ticket to Ride

    d. Come Together

TRAIN TRIVIA

#113. Where is "Train Street" located, where a train passes quickly through a narrow shops & residence area?

    a. Rome
    b. Paris
    c. Vietnam
    d. London

#114. What scale is the Guiness World Record holder for the smallest working train model?

    a. 1:200
    b. 1:1,100
    c. 1:12,000
    d. 1:35,200

#115. What is the name of the railway line which connects the Atlantic & Pacific coasts in the United States?

    a. Cross Country Express
    b. Transcontinental Railroad
    c. East/Way Railway
    d. Americana Rail

#116. What secondary use did the Jacobite Steam Train in Scotland have beyond regular train use?

    a. It transported royalty during their visit to Scotland
    b. It was used to portray the Hogwart's Express
    c. It was the leader's personal family train
    d. It was made into a 3d art exhibition

#117. What is the cost of a new diesel-electric locomotive in 2023?
    a. $1-3 million
    b. $2-5 million
    c. $7-10 million
    d. Over $15 million

#118. One of the earliest steam locomotives, Tom Thumb, was beat in a speed race by what animal?
    a. cheetah
    b. white-tailed deer
    c. horse
    d. cow

#119. Which historical event popularized the Pullman car?
    a. D-Day
    b. Teddy Roosevelt inauguration
    c. Abraham Lincoln assassination
    d. Bombing of Pearl Harbor

#120. Who instituted time zones in the United States?
    a. President Herbert Hoover
    b. Representatives from all U.S. railways
    c. Congress
    d. President John F. Kennedy

TRAIN TRIVIA

#121. What year did the number of U.S. railways peak?
    a. 1889
    b. 1916
    c. 1924
    d. 1946

#122. What railway job do you need to perform before being considered for an engineer position?
    a. Brakeman
    b. Yard Manager
    c. Conductor
    d. Dispatcher

#123. Who is considered the "father of railroads" in U.S.?
    a. George Stephenson
    b. William Henry Barlow
    c. John Stephens
    d. Richard Trevithick

#124. Which of the following is not a real singer/band with a train-related name?
    a. Boxcar Willie
    b. Grand Funk Railroad
    c. Train
    d. Midnight Train

TRAIN TRIVIA

#125. Which is a type of railroad signal?
   a. Ball signal
   b. Block signal
   c. Pullchain signal
   d. a and b

#126. In 1891, the first model train sets were for sale in which country?
   a. England
   b. United States
   c. Germany
   d. Belgium

#127. In Cuba, railroads were built to transport what?
   a. Sugar
   b. Tourists
   c. Rum
   d. Livestock

#128. What color were first class Russian trains painted?
   a. Red
   b. Blue
   c. Yellow
   d. Black

TRAIN TRIVIA

#129. In the 1930s, The Flying Hamburger train was located where?
    a. Luxembourg
    b. Russian
    c. Germany
    d. United States

#130. Which 1987 train comedy was inspired by the 1951 movie "Strangers On A Train"?
    a. Unstoppable
    b. Planes, Trains and Automobiles
    c. Throw Momma From The Train
    d. Bullet Train

#131. In 1971, railroads in Greece did this?
    a. Went on strike
    b. Became obsolete
    c. Became state-owned
    d. Went bankrupt

#132. The most common train engine currently used in the U.S. is?
    a. magnet-powered
    b. diesel
    c. electric
    d. steam

TRAIN TRIVIA

#133. The Ferdinand Magellan was a special armored train car made for which American President?
- a. John F. Kennedy
- b. Franklin Roosevelt
- c. Ronald Reagan
- d. Herbert Hoover

#134. The first American President to campaign by train was?
- a. Abraham Lincoln
- b. William Henry Harrison
- c. John Adams
- d. Franklin D. Roosevelt

#135. An average daily salary for working building railroads in the U.S. in the mid to late 1800s was?
- a. $1/day
- b. $2.50/day
- c. $10/day
- d. $46/day

#136. Average salary for a train engineer in the U.S. in 2023 is how much per year?
- a. $51,000
- b. $62,000
- c. $79,000
- d. $104,000

TRAIN TRIVIA

#137. The minimum age in the U.S. to be a train engineer is how old?

    a. 18
    b. 21
    c. 25
    d. 30

#138. The minimum degree required to be a U.S. train engineer is?

    a. high school diploma or GED equivalent
    b. 4 year college B.S. degree
    c. B.S. college degree + 2 yr master's degree
    d. B.S. college degree + 4 yr railroad program degree

#139. What % of current American train engineers are women?

    a. less than 1%
    b. 6%
    c. 19%
    d. 37%

#140. The most expensive model train engine sold at auction in 2006 for how much?

    a. $19,700
    b. $84,000
    c. $250,000
    d. $317,600

TRAIN TRIVIA

#141. The world's largest model railway is located in?
   a. San Diego, California
   b. Hamburg, Germany
   c. Geneva, Switzerland
   d. Bruges, Belgium

#142. The world's first model railway was built for whom?
   a. John Rockefeller's 8 year old son
   b. Emperor Napoleon III's 3 year old son
   c. George Washington's 6 year old nephew
   d. Henry Ford's 11 year old younger brother

#143. The world's largest model railway was built with over a million hours of labor and cost over $42 million. What is it's name?
   a. The Royal Train Collection
   b. Miniatur Wunderland
   c. Stephenson Curated Collection (SCC)
   d. New York Museum Model Train Display

#144. How much do Americans spend annually on model trains and accessories?
   a. $16 million
   b. $94 million
   c. $317 million
   d. $897 million

#145. Who was the first American President to switch from steam to diesel locomotives?
- a. Lyndon B. Johnson
- b. Franklin D. Roosevelt
- c. John F. Kennedy
- d. Abraham Lincoln

#146. Before dining cars existed, how did passengers get food while on a train?
- a. They packed picnic food from home
- b. Food was not allowed on the train
- c. Trains stopped at restaurants along the route
- d. Train workers would bring extra food for passengers

#147. Maglev trains are only currently used in which three countries?
- a. Japan, Germany, United States
- b. China, Japan, Korea
- c. Germany, Belgium, China
- d. Italy, China, Korea

#148. The ceremonial "Golden Spike" from the connection of the Transcontinental Railroad is worth what today?
- a. $610,000
- b. $1.2 million
- c. $2.2 million
- d. $7 million

TRAIN TRIVIA

#149. Which phone company started as "Southern Pacific Railroad Internal Network Communications"?
    a. Verizon
    b. Southern Bell
    c. Sprint
    d. US Cellular

#150. What typical vehicle feature is not on trains?
    a. Steering wheels
    b. Seatbelts
    c. Airbags
    d. All of the above

#151. What is the name of the world's shortest railway?
    a. Premier Line
    b. Angel's Flight
    c. The Vatican
    d. Fenelon Place Elevator

#152. Who is the author of the train-related poem entitled "The Railway Train"?
    a. Mary Oliver
    b. Maya Angelou
    c. Virginia Woolf
    d. Emily Dickinson

TRAIN TRIVIA

#153. Which celebrity appeared in Lionel Train commercials in the 1970s?
- a. Bruce Springsteen
- b. Johnny Cash
- c. Willie Nelson
- d. Jack Nicholson

#154. Which of the following are train enthusiasts?
- a. Michael Jordan
- b. Rod Stewart
- c. Frank Sinatra
- d. all of the above

#155. Which actor voiced the conductor in the 2004 movie The Polar Express?
- a. Vin Diesel
- b. Tom Hanks
- c. Brad Pitt
- d. Gene Hackman

#156. The Blue Train in South Africa has had which of these celebrities take it for a ride?
- a. Nelson Mandela
- b. Elton John
- c. both a and b
- d. neither a or b

TRAIN TRIVIA

#157. Which locomotive engineer became famous as a folk hero after he died in a train crash?
    a. Willie Sanderson
    b. Casey Jones
    c. George Stephenson
    d. Benjamin Smith

#158. In it's first 12 years, the Panama Railroad carried what value in gold nuggets, gold dust and gold coin?
    a. $194 million
    b. $230 million
    c. $647 million
    d. $750 million

#159. Which railroad company will haul your privately owned train car for you?
    a. CSX
    b. Baltimore & Ohio
    c. Milwaukee Road
    d. Amtrak

#160. Which singer was part of an investment group which bought Lionel Trains in the 1990s?
    a. Ringo Starr
    b. Neil Young
    c. George Strait
    d. Frank Sinatra

TRAIN TRIVIA

#161. Which American businessman left school at 11 years old and made a fortune in railroads?
- a. Andrew Carnegie
- b. Cornelius Vanderbilt
- c. John D. Rockefeller
- d. J. Paul Getty

#162. Roundhouses are built around what yard feature?
- a. Track switches
- b. Turntables
- c. Junkyards
- d. Railyard ponds

#163. The slang term "black hole" means what?
- a. Tender
- b. Boiler
- c. Tanker car
- d. Tunnel

#164. What was the name of the steam train in the sitcom "Petticoat Junction"?
- a. Petticoat Express
- b. Hooterville Cannonball
- c. Shady Rest Rail Co.
- d. Hooterville Railway

TRAIN TRIVIA

#165. What does the slang term "banjo" mean related to steam trains?
- a. Engineers would bring a banjo to play in downtime
- b. Firemen's shovels were called "banjos"
- c. Banjo was a term used for the brakeman
- d. "Banjo!" was called out when the trains were ready

#166. Where was the "beehive" in a railyard (slang)?
- a. Turntable
- b. Railroad yard office
- c. Terminal
- d. Bathroom area

#167. Turntables are still mainly used where in the world?
- a. Asia
- b. Europe
- c. United States
- d. Australia

#168. The Wabash Cannonball Train made a stop in which American city?
- a. Chicago, Illinois
- b. St. Louis, Missouri
- c. Little Rock, Arkansas
- d. El Paso, Texas

TRAIN TRIVIA

#169. In 1865, the Abraham Lincoln funeral train passed through how many cities?
- a. 64
- b. 97
- c. 180
- d. 440

#170. Which family board game allows you to own railroads?
- a. Sorry
- b. A Ticket to Ride
- c. Monopoly
- d. RailPlay

#171. Which country has had the most train robberies throughout history?
- a. Germany
- b. Japan
- c. Australia
- d. United States

#172. How long after the United States imported it's first steam locomotive from England did it build it's own?
- a. The same year
- b. Two years later
- c. Within five years
- d. About 10 years later

TRAIN TRIVIA

#173. What did the expansion of the railroads assist?
    a. Military supply transport
    b. Passenger leisure travel
    c. Mail express transport
    d. All of the above

#174. What is railroad gauge?
    a. A tool for maintaining railroad tracks
    b. Measure of the width between two rails
    c. A strong metal used to forge steel tracks
    d. A coating put on railroad tracks for grip

#175. What is a berth on a train?
    a. When a baby is born during a train trip
    b. The area where the luggage is stored
    c. A sleeping compartment
    d. The kitchen of the dining car

#176. The first rails used in Germany for a mining cart were made of which material?
    a. Tin
    b. Wood
    c. Steel
    d. Composite

TRAIN TRIVIA

#177. What is the value of freight stolen from trains during 2023 in U.S. alone?
   a. $124,000
   b. $792,000
   c. $2.6 million
   d. $130 million

#178. Another name for continuous welded rail is?
   a. Straightline Rails
   b. Infinite Rails
   c. Ribbon Rails
   d. Stream Rails

#179. In 1870, U.S. railroads began giving these to employees?
   a. Train engineer license
   b. Uniforms
   c. Free meals
   d. Discounted train tickets

#180. What was the first named train worldwide?
   a. Tom Thumb
   b. Iron Horse
   c. Irish Mail
   d. Stephenson Special

TRAIN TRIVIA

#181. What is the largest railway museum worldwide?
  a. Illinois Railway Museum
  b. National Railway Museum
  c. Heritage Rail Museum
  d. Smithsonian Rail Museum

#182. The location of the cowcatcher on a train is?
  a. On top of the engine
  b. On the lower front of the engine
  c. On the upper back of the engine
  d. Under the engine between wheels and rails

#183. What year were the first freight cars built and used on the railroads?
  a. 1804
  b. 1832
  c. 1869
  d. 1892

#184. What symbol was featured in the Pennsylvania Railroad's logo?
  a. Forge
  b. Keystone
  c. Steam engine
  d. Owl

#185. What was the first major addition to freight car construction?

    a. Sidewalls
    b. Sprung wheels
    c. Unload chutes
    d. Door locks

#186. What feature of later American freight cars was never before seen on British freight cars?

    a. Enclosed freight cars
    b. Fortified wheels
    c. Stabilizer bars
    d. Temperature control

#187. The Empire Builder train ran between Seattle and Portland on the west and which city in the East?

    a. Boston
    b. Milwaukee
    c. Kansas City
    d. Chicago

#188. What happened to the Soo Line Railroad in the 2000s?

    a. It went bankrupt
    b. It was consolidated by CP
    c. It was sold to a European rail company and moved
    d. It was converted to a short line

TRAIN TRIVIA

#189. One locomotive weighs as much as about how many hippos?
- a. 64
- b. 91
- c. 108
- d. 117

#190. What is a "dinky line" in railroading?
- a. Miniature model train layout
- b. A short railroad, usually operated by short trains
- c. Railroad that is new and small scale
- d. Slang term for amusement park passenger trains

#191. Which city calls their train system the "L"?
- a. Dallas
- b. San Francisco
- c. Chicago
- d. New York

#192. What is the cost of the most expensive rail infrastructure project ever (located in England)?
- a. $84 million
- b. $610 million
- c. $34 billion
- d. $86 billion

TRAIN TRIVIA

#193. Which railroad in the U.S. has the most trains with 8,300 in their fleet?
    a. CSX
    b. Canadian Pacific
    c. BNSF
    d. Union Pacific

#194. What is a name for an "uphill train"?
    a. Cliff railway
    b. Funicular railway
    c. Inclined plane railway
    d. All of the above

#195. Which four U.S. states have no Amtrak service?
    a. Rhode Island, Alaska, Hawaii, New Mexico
    b. Hawaii, Alaska, North Dakota, New Jersey
    c. Kentucky, Hawaii, Rhode Island, Wyoming
    d. Hawaii, Alaska, South Dakota, Wyoming

#196. Which U.S. railroad currently uses the slogan "How Tomorrow Moves"?
    a. Baltimore & Ohio
    b. Milwaukee Road
    c. CSX
    d. Union Pacific

TRAIN TRIVIA

#197. Which animal is the original mascot of Chessie?
    a. Cheetah
    b. Playful puppy
    c. Climbing mountain goat
    d. Sleeping kitten

#198. The word "Train" comes from a word in _____ language which means to draw or drag?
    a. Italian
    b. Greek
    c. French
    d. Chinese

#199. America's railway system features approximately how many railroad ties?
    a. 64 million
    b. 213 million
    c. 489 million
    d. 615 million

#200. How many gallons of fuel does it take a train to move 1 ton of freight weight for 500 miles?
    a. 1 gallon of fuel
    b. 13 gallons of fuel
    c. 18 gallons of fuel
    d. 27 gallons of fuel

TRAIN TRIVIA

#201. If 10% of truck freight were moved by train instead, savings would equal planting how many trees?
 a. 642,000
 b. 12 million
 c. 86 million
 d. 300 million

#202. What percentage of Class 1 U.S. rail workers are union members?
 a. 60%
 b. 72%
 c. 85%
 d. 97%

#203. In 2024, the average U.S. rail worker earns how much in total compensation annually?
 a. $72,000
 b. $87,500
 c. $101,700
 d. $160,000

#204. Which city has been the busiest rail hub in the U.S. for over 150 years?
 a. Indianapolis
 b. Chicago
 c. Milwaukee
 d. New York City

TRAIN TRIVIA

#205. Every year freight trains haul an average of how many tons of freight per American citizen?

    a. 17 tons
    b. 61 tons
    c. 79 tons
    d. 142 tons

#206. One railcar can carry enough flour to bake how many loaves of bread?

    a. 258,000
    b. 310,000
    c. 323,000
    d. 349,000

#207. Which grain is the one most frequently carried by American railroads?

    a. barley
    b. oats
    c. corn
    d. wheat

#208. What percentage of coal deliveries to power plants are carried by railroads in the U.S.?

    a. 70%
    b. 75%
    c. 80%
    d. 90%

TRAIN TRIVIA

#209. How many railcars full of construction, pulp and paper products are hauled by U.S. railroads annually?
    a. 1 million
    b. 2.3 million
    c. 2.6 million
    d. 3 million

#210. One rail carries enough crude oil to make how many gallons of gasoline?
    a. 13,500
    b. 18,000
    c. 21,300
    d. 27,000

#211. Each year, railroads carry what percentage of new cars and trucks throughout the U.S. to dealerships?
    a. 70%
    b. 75%
    c. 80%
    d. 95%

#212. When the Transcontinental Railroad was completed, how long was the trip from San Francisco to New York?
    a. 4 days
    b. 1 week
    c. 2 weeks
    d. 1 month

TRAIN TRIVIA

#213. Building the Transcontinental Railroad cost $60 million in 1860s, how much is that in today's money?
- a. $800 million
- b. $1.2 billion
- c. $1.6 billion
- d. $2 billion

#214. The Disneyland monorail system was first in America in 1959 and based on what country's system?
- a. France
- b. Japan
- c. Germany
- d. Canada

#215. How many Walt Disney World guests ride the monorail system annually?
- a. 17 million
- b. 50 million
- c. 84 million
- d. 107 million

#216. How many miles of monorail track are there at WDW?
- a. 9 miles
- b. 14 miles
- c. 21 miles
- d. 54 miles

TRAIN TRIVIA

#217. How many people pass through Grand Central Station daily?
- a. 94,000
- b. 231,000
- c. 564,000
- d. 750,000

#218. Which train station has the most platforms of any on the planet (44 platforms)?
- a. Beijing Fengtai
- b. Waterloo (London)
- c. Roma Termini
- d. Grand Central Station

#219. A 13 foot wide clock with the world's largest display of Tiffany glass is featured in which famous train station?
- a. Antwerp Central Station
- b. Kanazawa Station
- c. Grand Central Station
- d. Flinders Street Station

#220. The American National Rail Network is how many times as large as the European Rail System?
- a. 2x
- b. 4x
- c. 7x
- d. 1

#1. Which locomotive holds the record for the heaviest steam locomotive ever built?

a. Union Pacific Big Boy

#2. Which country was the first to introduce the concept of high-speed rail?

a. Japan

#3. What is the maximum speed of the Shanghai Maglev (fastest train in the world)?

d. 375 mph

#4. What is the world's first commercial monorail system named?

a. Wuppertal Suspension Railway

#5. What was the steepest operating mainline grade in the U.S. until 2001 when it was removed from service?

a. 4.7% Saluda Grade (North Carolina)

#6. What is the name of the first high-speed rail system in the United States?

a. Acela Express

#7. What locomotive set the 1938 steam locomotive world speed record?

a. Mallard

#8. What country boasts the world's highest express railway line?

a. China

#9. What is the name of the world's longest railway tunnel?

a. Gotthard Base Tunnel

#10. Which train holds the record for the fastest commercial train service in the world?

a. Maglev

#11. What is the name of the train that connects Paris to Istanbul?

a. Orient Express

#12. What is the highest recorded speed record for a steam locomotive?

b. 126mph by Mallard

#13. What is the name of the oldest surviving steam locomotive in the world?

a. Puffing Billy

#14. What was the name of the first steam locomotive to run on rails in the United States?

b. Tom Thumb

#15. What steam locomotive pulled Abraham Lincoln's funeral train?

d. Old Nashville

#16. Which steam locomotive is the largest and most powerful ever built?

a. Big Boy

#17. Which Art Deco design diesel locomotive served on the Chicago, Burlington and Quincy Railroad?

b. Zephyr

#18. Which famous steam locomotive pulled the Freedom Train during WW2?

d. Reading T-1

ANSWERS

#19. Which is known for it's fleet of heritage locomotives, each painted in a different historic paint scheme?
a. Union Pacific

#20. What is the purpose of the locomotive's horn?
c. To warn pedestrians and vehicles at crossings

#21. Which is known for it's yellow bonnet locomotives?
c. BNSF Railway

#22. What part of a train's system helps the train slow down or stop?
c. Brake Shoe

#23. Which type of railcar is used for carrying liquids like oil or chemicals?
c. Tank Car

#24. What connects train cars together?
a. Coupler

#25. Which famous train travels a luxurious route from Cape Town to Pretoria?
a. Blue Train

#26. Who developed the first practical steam locomotive boiler which improved steam engine efficiency?
c. Richard Trevithick

#27. What purpose does a cowcatcher (pilot) serve?
c. To deflect debris from the track

#28. Which part of a steam locomotive distributes steam to the cylinders to move the train?
d. Valve gear

#29. Which railroad operated the famous "Super Chief" train from Chicago to Los Angeles?
d. Santa Fe

#30. Which part stores and supplies coal or oil to the firebox on a train?
b. Tender

#31. Which company operated the Hiawatha train?
d. Milwaukee Road

#32. In the United States, what is the freight train length legal limit?

b. there is no legal limit

#33. Which is not a real Canadian railroad?

c. Alberta Road

#34. "Folsom Prison Blues" and _____ were train hits by singer Johnny Cash

c. Train of Love

#35. Which famous train was featured in a 1954 film starring Marlon Brando (and also the film name)?

c. The Wild One

#36. What is the most common scale for model trains?

a. HO scale

#37. What does the term "DCC" stand for in model railroading?

a. Digital Command Control

#38. Which material is commonly used for the scenery on a model train layout?
d. All of the above

#39. In the famous Harry Potter book series, what is the name of the train which takes students to school?
b. Hogwarts Express

#40. What is a "yard goat" in train slang?
a. Small locomotive used for moving cars in yard

#41. Which scale is larger, HO or N?
a. HO

#42. The box with windows on top of a caboose roof is called what?
c. Cupola

#43. How many passenger platforms does Grand Central Station in New York City have?
c. 44

#44. During the peak of the Trans-Siberian Railway construction during the 1890s, how many workers were employed?
b. 85,000

#45. Which of these railfans created the Thomas the Tank Engine series for his son?
b. Reverend W. Awdry

#46. Which of these helps overcome the obstacle of altitude/height on a railroad
b. Switchback

#47. Signal systems not only are used to communicate the speed of a train but also the what?
b. Route

#48. What train feature is now obsolete?
c. Caboose

#49. Which train became famous for being the target of a train robbery in the U.S. in 1877?
b. Union Pacific No. 119

#50. What was the name of the first luxury sleeping car introduced in 1865 in America?

a. Pullman Car

#51. Which country was the first to introduce regular passenger train services in 1830?

c. United Kingdom

#52. What was the original purpose of the invention of the first trains in the early 19th century?

c. Freight transportation

#53. Which technology does the Shanghai Maglev Train utilize?

d. Magnetic levitation

#54. Which country is home to Thalys, a high-speed rail service known for it's red trains?

c. Belgium

#55. Which train part controls the flow of steam to the cylinders to propel the train?

b. Regulator

#56. Which company was known for it's luxury "Broadway Limited" train?
d. Pennsylvania Railroad

#57. Who invented the steam whistle?
d. Adrian Stephens

#58. Most modern rail cars can have a gross weight of how many pounds each?
c. 286,000

#59. When a train uses it's version of "cruise control", what percent of fuel savings results?
c. 3-5%

#60. How many tons of freight do American railroads haul each year?
d. 1.7 billion tons

#61. How many railroads currently operate in the U.S.?
d. Over 600

#62. Some locomotives have a Positive Train Control (PTC) system onboard which does what?

c. Automatically stops a train to avoid collisions

#63. These are used to help in the maintenance of railroad tracks in the U.S.?

b. Drones

#64. The name of the platform for the locomotive driver is called the what?

d. Footplate

#65. What is the job title of the train driver?

c. Engineer

#66. What year did the Great Train Robbery occur?

c. 1963

#67. What is the train number on the side of the Thomas the Tank Engine Character?

c. 1

#68. On average, railroads are how many times more efficient than semi trucks?

b. 3-4x

#69. A single train can carry the same amount as how many semi freight trucks?

d. 300

#70. Amtrak began operations in which year?

c. 1971

#71. Which was never used as an Amtrak promotional campaign slogan?

c. "Training To The Future"

#72. On an average day, Amtrak carries how many passengers systemwide?

c. 89,000

#73. The Empire Builder makes how many stops over 8 states on it's route?

a. 40

#74. How many Amtrak stations are listed as National Historic Places?

b. three

#75. The smallest community in the U.S. served by Amtrak has how many residents?

a. 5

#76. The fastest train in the Western Hemisphere is what?

a. Acela

#77. Which country has the largest railway network in the world?

b. United States

#78. How many miles of railroad track are in the U.S.?

c. 155,000

#79. In the U.S. rail network, what is the % of freight routes to passenger routes?

d. 80% freight / 20% passenger

#80. Which is the oldest railway in the world still in use since 1758?

b. Middleton Railway (Leeds, England)

ANSWERS

#81. The longest journey you can take by train crosses 2 continents from Portugal to Singapore at a cost of:

b. $1,300

#82. The longest direct train service in the world is in Russia on the Trans-Siberian route. What is the total time, mileage and stops on this direct route?

c. 166 hrs / 5,772 miles / 142 stops

#83. America's oldest operating railroad (1832) is named?

a. Strasburg Railroad

#84. Shinjuku Station in Tokyo, Japan is the world's busiest train station with how many daily passengers?

d. 3.6 million

#85. In what year were Australia's coasts linked for travel by train:

a. 1917

#86. Which train travels on the world's longest straight stretch of railroad, spanning 303 miles?

b. Indian Pacific

#87. The highest railway bridge in the world stands 98 feet higher than the Eiffel Tower and is located where?

d. India

#88. The longest train station name is "Llanfairpwllgwyngyllgogerychwyrndrobwllllantysil iogogogoch" and is located where?

c. Wales, England

#89. Which countries currently have no railway system:

d. all of the above

#90. How many miles of railway track are there in the entire world?

d. 1 million

#91. Under Grand Central Station there is a secret train platform known as what?

b. Track 61

#92. Extreme temperatures, such as what temps can cause steel railroad tracks to buckle?

c. Over 100 degrees F

#93. In the early 2000s, New York City disposed of how many old subway trains by sinking them in the ocean:

d. 2,580

#94. In the U.S., how often is a person or vehicle hit by a train?

b. every three hours

#95. In the U.S., who owns the railroad tracks?

c. train companies

#96. When a freight train is traveling at 55 mph, how long does it take it to stop?

b. 1 mile

#97. What percentage of train routes in England go through London?

c. 70%

#98. The total contact between train wheels and track is the size of what?

c. silver dollar

ANSWERS

#99. The longest train station platform in England is the size of how many football fields?

c. six

#100. How many feet long does the Big Boy engine measure?

c. 132 feet

#101. How much horsepower did the most powerful steam engines (like Big Boy) generate at peak output?

c. over 6000 hp

#102. Big Boy engine was designed to move large amounts of freight during which war for Union Pacific?

d. WW2

#103. Amtrak trains typically run at what range of speed?

b. 80 - 125 mph

#104. What does the word "intermodal" mean?

c. freight is moved via 2+ methods (ship, train, truck, plane)

#105. What is the nickname for the Japanese Shinkansen high-speed train?

b. Bullet train

#106.What city in the U.S. has the oldest and steepest funicular railway you can still ride?

c. Pittsburgh

#107. Gordon, James, Percy & Emily are all characters from what popular children's train book series?

b. Thomas The Tank Engine

#108. The raised observation seat in the caboose car was sometimes called the "_____'s Seat"?

b. Angel

#109. The oldest subway tunnel in North America is located in which city?

c. Boston

#110. The world's oldest continuously operating streetcar line is located in which city?

c. New Orleans

#111. Stephenson's Rocket was not a spaceship, but an earlier form of what type of vehicle?

b. Steam train

#112. Which rail-based "2004 Board Game of the Year" shares it's name with a Beatles song?

c. Ticket to Ride

#113. Where is "Train Street" located, where a train passes quickly through a narrow shops & residence area?

c. Vietnam

#114. What scale is the Guiness World Record holder for the smallest working train model?

d. 1:35,200

#115. What is the name of the railway line which connects the Atlantic & Pacific coasts in the United States?

b. Transcontinental Railroad

#116. What secondary use did the Jacobite Steam Train in Scotland have beyond regular train use?

b. It was used to portray the Hogwart's Express

#117. What is the cost of a new diesel-electric locomotive in 2023?

b. $2-5 million

#118. One of the earliest steam locomotives, Tom Thumb, was beat in a speed race by what animal?

c. horse

#119. Which historical event popularized the Pullman car?

c. Abraham Lincoln assassination

#120. Who instituted time zones in the United States?

b. Representatives from all U.S. railways

#121. What year did the number of U.S. railways peak?

b. 1916

#122. What railway job do you need to perform before being considered for an engineer position?

c. Conductor

#123. Who is considered the "father of railroads" in U.S.?

c. John Stephens

#124. Which of the following is not a real singer/band with a train-related name?
d. Midnight Train

#125. Which is a type of railroad signal?
d. a and b

#126. In 1891, the first model train sets were for sale in which country?
c. Germany

#127. In Cuba, railroads were built to transport what?
a. Sugar

#128. What color were first class Russian trains painted?
b. Blue

#129. In the 1930s, The Flying Hamburger train was located where?
c. Germany

#130. Which 1987 train comedy was inspired by the 1951 movie "Strangers On A Train"?
c. Throw Momma From The Train

ANSWERS

#131. In 1971, railroads in Greece did this?
c. Became state-owned

#132. The most common train engine currently used in the U.S. is?
b. diesel

#133. The Ferdinand Magellan was a special armored train car made for which American President?
b. Franklin Roosevelt

#134. The first American President to campaign by train was?
d. Franklin D. Roosevelt

#135. An average daily salary for working building railroads in the U.S. in the mid to late 1800s was?
b. $2.50/day

#136. Average salary for a train engineer in the U.S. in 2023 is how much per year?
b. $62,000

#137. The minimum age in the U.S. to be a train engineer is how old?

b. 21

#138. The minimum degree required to be a U.S. train engineer is?

a. high school diploma or GED equivalent

#139. What % of current American train engineers are women?

c. 19%

#140. The most expensive model train engine sold at auction in 2006 for how much?

c. $250,000

#141. The world's largest model railway is located in?

b. Hamburg, Germany

#142. The world's first model railway was built for whom?

b. Emperor Napoleon III's 3 year old son

ANSWERS

#143.The world's largest model railway was built with over a million hours of labor and cost over $42 million. What is it's name?

b. Miniatur Wunderland

#144. How much do Americans spend annually on model trains and accessories?

d. $897 million

#145. Who was the first American President to switch from steam to diesel locomotives?

b. Franklin D. Roosevelt

#146. Before dining cars existed, how did passengers get food while on a train?

c. Trains stopped at restaurants along the route

#147. Maglev trains are only currently used in which three countries?

b. China, Japan, Korea

#148. The ceremonial "Golden Spike" from the connection of the Transcontinental Railroad is worth what today?

c. $2.2 million

#149. Which phone company started as "Southern Pacific Railroad Internal Network Communications"?
c. Sprint

#150. What typical vehicle feature is not on trains?
d. All of the above

#151. What is the name of the world's shortest railway?
b. Angel's Flight

#152. Who is the author of the train-related poem entitled "The Railway Train"?
d. Emily Dickinson

#153. Which celebrity appeared in Lionel Train commercials in the 1970s?
b. Johnny Cash

#154. Which of the following are train enthusiasts?
d. all of the above

#155. Which actor voiced the conductor in the 2004 movie The Polar Express?
b. Tom Hanks

#156. The Blue Train in South Africa has had which of these celebrities take it for a ride?
c. both a and b

#157. Which locomotive engineer became famous as a folk hero after he died in a train crash?
b. Casey Jones

#158. In it's first 12 years, the Panama Railroad carried what value in gold nuggets, gold dust and gold coin?
d. $750 million

#159. Which railroad company will haul your privately owned train car for you?
d. Amtrak

#160.Which singer was part of an investment group which bought Lionel Trains in the 1990s?
b. Neil Young

#161. Which American businessman left school at 11 years old and made a fortune in railroads?
b. Cornelius Vanderbilt

#162. Roundhouses are built around what yard feature?
b. Turntables

#163. The slang term "black hole" means what?
d. Tunnel

#164. What was the name of the steam train in the sitcom "Petticoat Junction"?
b. Hooterville Cannonball

#165. What does the slang term "banjo" mean related to steam trains?
b. Firemen's shovels were called "banjos"

#166. Where was the "beehive" in a railyard (slang)?

b. Railroad yard office

#167. Turntables are still mainly used where in the world?

c. United States

#168. The Wabash Cannonball Train made a stop in which American city?

b. St. Louis, Missouri

#169. In 1865, the Abraham Lincoln funeral train passed through how many cities?

d. 440

#170. Which family board game allows you to own railroads?

c. Monopoly

#171. Which country has had the most train robberies throughout history?

d. United States

#172. How long after the United States imported it's first steam locomotive from England did it build it's own?

a. The same year

#173. What did the expansion of the railroads assist?

d. All of the above

#174. What is railroad gauge?

b. Measure of the width between two rails

#175. What is a berth on a train?

c. A sleeping compartment

#176. The first rails used in Germany for a mining cart were made of which material?

b. Wood

#177.What is the value of freight stolen from trains during 2023 in U.S. alone?

d. $130 million

#178. Another name for continuous welded rail is?

c. Ribbon Rails

#179. In 1870, U.S. railroads began giving these to employees?

b. Uniforms

ANSWERS

#180. What was the first named train worldwide?

c. Irish Mail

#181. What is the largest railway museum worldwide?

b. National Railway Museum

#182. The location of the cowcatcher on a train is?

b. On the lower front of the engine

#183.What year were the first freight cars built and used on the railroads?

b. 1832

#184. What symbol was featured in the Pennsylvania Railroad's logo?

b. Keystone

#185. What was the first major addition to freight car construction?

b. Sprung wheels

#186. What feature of later American freight cars was never before seen on British freight cars?

a. Enclosed freight cars

#187. The Empire Builder train ran between Seattle and Portland on the west and which city in the East?
d. Chicago

#188. What happened to the Soo Line Railroad in the 2000s?
b. It was consolidated by CP

#189. One locomotive weighs as much as about how many hippos?
c. 108

#190. What is a "dinky line" in railroading?
b. A short railroad, usually operated by short trains

#191. Which city calls their train system the "L"?
c. Chicago

#192. What is the cost of the most expensive rail infrastructure project ever (located in England)?
d. $86 billion

#193. Which railroad in the U.S. has the most trains with 8,300 in their fleet?
d. Union Pacific

#194. What is a name for an "uphill train"?
d. All of the above

#195. Which four U.S. states have no Amtrak service?
d. Hawaii, Alaska, South Dakota, Wyoming

#196. Which U.S. railroad currently uses the slogan "How Tomorrow Moves"?
c. CSX

#197. Which animal is the original mascot of Chessie?
d. Sleeping kitten

#198. The word "Train" comes from a word in _____ language which means to draw or drag?
c. French

#199. America's railway system features approximately how many railroad ties?
c. 489 million

#200. How many gallons of fuel does it take a train to move 1 ton of freight weight for 500 miles?
a. 1 gallon of fuel

#201. If 10% of truck freight were moved by train instead, savings would equal planting how many trees?
d. 300 million

#202. What percentage of Class 1 U.S. rail workers are union members?
c. 85%

#203. In 2024, the average U.S. rail worker earns how much in total compensation annually?
d. $160,000

#204. Which city has been the busiest rail hub in the U.S. for over 150 years?
b. Chicago

#205. Every year freight trains haul an average of how many tons of freight per American citizen?
b. 61 tons

#206. One railcar can carry enough flour to bake how many loaves of bread?
a. 258,000

#207. Which grain is the one most frequently carried by American railroads?

c. corn

#208. What percentage of coal deliveries to power plants are carried by railroads in the U.S.?

a. 70%

#209. How many railcars full of construction, pulp and paper products are hauled by U.S. railroads annually?

d. 3 million

#210. One rail carries enough crude oil to make how many gallons of gasoline?

a. 13,500

#211. Each year, railroads carry what percentage of new cars and trucks throughout the U.S. to dealerships?

c. 80%

#212. When the Transcontinental Railroad was completed, how long was the trip from San Francisco to New York?

b. 1 week

#213. Building the Transcontinental Railroad cost $60 million in 1860s, how much is that in today's money?

b. $1.2 billion

#214. The Disneyland monorail system was first in America in 1959 and based on what country's system?

c. Germany

#215. How many Walt Disney World guests ride the monorail system annually?

b. 50 million

#216. How many miles of monorail track are there at WDW?

b. 14 miles

#217. How many people pass through Grand Central Station daily?

d. 750,000

#218. Which train station has the most platforms of any on the planet (44 platforms)?

d. Grand Central Station

#219. A 13 foot wide clock with the world's largest display of Tiffany glass is featured in which famous train station?

c. Grand Central Station

#220. The American National Rail Network is how many times as large as the European Rail System?

a. 2x